SHIRE NATURAL HIS

C000282723

THE
WREN

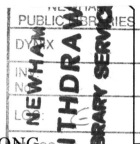

EDWARD A. ARMSTRONG

CONTENTS

Cover: *A wren at its nest.*

Series editor: Jim Flegg.

Revised after the author's death by his son,
Patrick H. Armstrong

British Library Cataloguing in Publication Data:
Armstrong, Edward A.
The wren.
I. Title.
598.834

...ain by C. I. Thomas & Sons (Haverfordwest) Ltd,
...erlins Bridge, Haverfordwest, Dyfed SA61 1XF.

Introduction

This book gives an account of the way in which members of one particular species of organism, the wren, live: it describes how the form, colouration, environment, behaviour and way of life of that species are interrelated; and it shows how the biology, and particularly the breeding habits, of this common European bird are closely related to the habitat.

Wrens are found in woodlands and suburban gardens, on high mountains and remote islands, in hedgerows and in thickets. It is likely that many readers will themselves be able to study this lively little bird's brilliant song, watch its delightful courtship display and perhaps find its intricately constructed domed nests.

The wren (*Troglodytes troglodytes*), affectionately nicknamed 'Jenny Wren' or 'Kitty Wren' in parts of Britain, is one of the most interesting of all European birds and has fascinated our forefathers since prehistoric times. The folknames, sayings, legends and, in some places, ceremonies connected with it are evidence of this. It is easy to understand why the large and powerful eagle should be called the 'king of the birds', but why should the tiny, weak and inconspicuous wren also be called 'king' in many European languages? In Italian it is called *re d'uccelli*, 'king of birds'; in Dutch *Winterköning*, 'winter king'; in German *Zaunkönig, Mausekönig* and *Schneekönig*, 'hedge king', 'mouse king' and 'snow king'. The notion that the wren is royal is implicit also in older names: *basileus*, 'king', in Greek, and *regulus*, 'prince', in Latin.

The ancient fable of the competition between the birds as to who should be king is widely known. The eagle soared up, proudly confident of his supremacy, but a wren which had hidden itself on his back fluttered a little higher and claimed the crown. The other birds, disgusted at such trickery, condemned the wren to seek its food in crevices and low herbage. Such titles and tales might seem to be trivial folklore but for the fact that the wren has had an important role in ceremonies which date back to immemorial times and yet still survive. In the Republic of Ireland and the Isle of Man boys carry from cottage to cottage a caged wren or a toy representing it on St Stephen's Day, just after Christmas and the winter solstice. The latter, about 22nd December, coincides with the longest night and was formerly thought of as the time when the sun appears to pause before returning. As the 'Wren Boys' carried the wren or its emblem around the village, they sang traditional wren songs, seeking small contributions from the cottagers. Comparable ceremonies formerly took place in the south of England, and a more elaborate wren ritual was performed in the south of France. Piecing together all these clues, we find that the wren represented the powers of darkness, most evident at midwinter,

1. *A Shetland wren. Note the powerful bill and legs.*

while the eagle represented the powers of light and life, growth and goodness. Thus these ancient ceremonies may be interpreted as asserting belief in the triumph of all that is favourable to humankind's well-being.

RECOGNITION

The wren is easy to identify because no other small European bird living close to the ground looks so active and dumpy. The only other common small European species which also is mainly brown and frequents low vegetation is the hedge sparrow or dunnock (*Prunella modularis*), but this bird averages about 14.5 cm (5³/₄ inches) in length, compared with the wren's 9.5 cm (3³/₄ inches), and, unlike the wren, it does not frequently cock up its tail. The wren's plumage is somewhat reddish, with paler underparts, and there is a faint eyestripe. Male and female are similar in appearance, but when the male's wings and tail are outspread during courtship they are seen to be delicately barred in shades of brown. We are most likely to be sure of the presence of a wren when we hear its distinctive song, which is very loud for a small bird.

The wrens of the northern islands, such as Shetland, the Outer Hebrides, St Kilda, the Faroe Islands and Iceland, are each sufficiently distinct in appearance and size from the continental form to be regarded as different subspecies, but such differences are not obvious in the field.

The goldcrest (*Regulus regulus*) is even smaller than the wren, about 9 cm (3¹/₂ inches) in length, but has a conspicuous orange-yellow cap and tends to frequent conifers, especially yews.

OTHER WRENS

In the Americas, whence the wrens originally came, there are many different species. The majority are small, like the European wren, but some are larger. Most are readily recognisable as wrens: they are dumpy, have short tails, rounded wings and slender, slightly curved bills. Many are brownish, and striped or barred. They favour dense, often fairly low vegetation, and their presence is often revealed more through their song than through their appearance. Sometimes more than one species occurs in the same region, but in such cases they do not eat exactly the same foods. If they did, they would compete, and this might lead to the extinction of one of them. Two species which have distributions that meet in an area also tend to some extent to keep apart — to prefer different habitats. They are said to occupy different 'ecological niches.' Gradually, over thousands of years, differences between the species evolve, which adapt them to different parts of the environment, or for the selection of different kinds of prey.

In Europe, where there is just one species of wren, it has a wide range of habitats to itself: it is therefore at home in both 'fertile' and 'bleak' habitats. The European wren also lives in North America, but there it has to compete with the very similar house wren. The European wren (called the winter wren in America) has been restricted there to bleak habitats, while the house wren lives in the more productive, fertile places, including gardens.

In this way, through the adaptation of wren species to different habitats and foods, a variety of wren types has evolved. In the Americas they range in habitat from the understorey of deciduous forests, through thickets and gardens, to tropical rainforests. Wrens are also found in upland ravine habitats, along streamsides, in marshes and in desert, scrub and cliff environments. They show considerable variety in their mode of feeding. Cactus wrens overturn stones in the search for food. Song wrens seek prey by pushing up fallen leaves.

The breeding biology similarly varies. Only a few wrens have developed polygamous breeding: these include the house wrens and marsh wrens. In the banded-backed wren, birds other than the parents have sometimes been seen helping at the nest. In the house wren, which may lay several clutches in the course of the summer, young occasionally feed their younger siblings. Some wrens of tropical forests remain in monogamous pairs from year to year, and usually the hen alone incubates.

The often brilliantly coloured blue wrens or fairy wrens of Australia are *not* closely related.

2 (above). *Worldwide distribution of* Troglodytes troglodytes.

3 (below left). *Distribution of the wren in the British Isles. The distribution of some of the subspecies is shown.*

4 (below right). *The distribution of some of the subspecies of the wren in Europe and North Africa.*

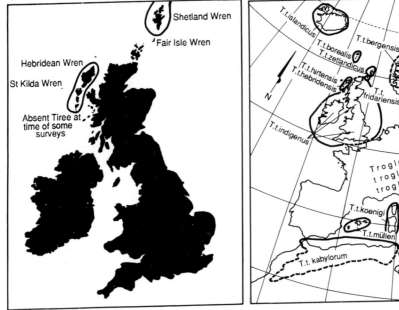

Range and lifestyle

DISTRIBUTION, DISPERSAL AND MIGRATION

The wren has succeeded in establishing populations throughout an enormous area of the world. Success is not always gained by the fierce and powerful! In Iceland it reaches almost to the Arctic Circle, and on the Norwegian coast some wrens breed north of it. Further south, there are two subspecies in the North African mountains, and there are wren populations on the larger Mediterranean islands, in Poland, Russia and Iran and across Asia to China and Japan. Some of these populations are migratory. Not only are there subspecies in Kamchatka and the groups of islands across the Bering Strait, but North American populations extend from the Aleutian Islands and Alaska into the Rocky Mountains and as far south in the United States as northern Georgia.

The wren is usually described as a 'partial migrant' because it is resident in some areas, but not in all. In Iceland it is sedentary. Although some breed as far north as 67° along the mild coast of Norway, they do not winter in northern Scandinavia, nor in Finland. There is a sparse breeding population in the forest of Bielowiecza in Poland, but the wrens seen there are believed to be wanderers from elsewhere. Probably, where wrens are sparsely distributed their survival in winter would be difficult because sufficient numbers are not available to 'cluster-roost' to keep each other warm (see below). In North America, the winter wren is a summer resident in Maine (43° to 47°N), common in coniferous forests but only rarely resident through the winter. In China some wrens winter as far south as Kwangtung. Wrens of mountain ranges, including those on British mountains, descend to lower levels in winter. There is also some evidence from ringing recoveries of southward movement of some British wrens towards the continent at the approach of winter.

There are only a few records indicating the great distances that identifiable ringed wrens have been known to travel. A nestling ringed near Berlin, Germany, one May, flew into a room in Périgueux, Dordogne, France, the following December — a distance of 1220 km (760 miles). Another, which may have come from Sweden, was ringed on Greifswalder Oie in the Baltic and was found nearly a year later at Como in northern Italy. Such records indicate how far-travelled birds could have established populations on isolated islands.

We know that the wren is, in origin, an American bird, because there are many species in the Americas, especially the warmer regions, but only one in Europe, Asia and North Africa. Of over sixty species commonly recognised, by far the majority are found in Central America. The family includes some notable songsters, such as the organ bird or quadrille wren of South America and the song wren of Central America. Some tropical species sing 'duets'. Several species, such as the cactus and canyon wrens, have adapted to life in the deserts of the south-western United States and Mexico.

Did some American wrens once fly across the Atlantic to Europe, establish themselves, and then spread eastwards? Although there is a record of one alighting on an eastbound ship some 350 km (220 miles) out in the Atlantic, this is not likely. Perhaps around eight thousand years ago, at the end of the ice age, there was sufficient vegetation in the area of the Bering Strait to harbour wrens, and the invasion came from the east. One reason for believing that the wren's dispersal may have been comparatively recent is that the song is readily recognisable wherever the bird occurs.

HABITAT AND POPULATION DENSITY

The wren, being exceptionally adaptable, is widespread in Europe but avoids very arid and heavily built-up areas. In Britain it nests from the coastline up to at least 750 metres (about 2500 feet), in North Africa at about 1800 metres (6000 feet), and in Kashmir at around 4600 metres (14,500 feet).

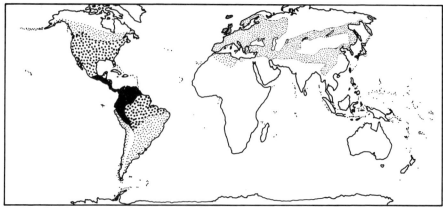

5. The distribution of the different species of the wren family. The intensity of the stippling is proportional to the number of species; most species occur in Central and South America.

The St Kilda subspecies (*Troglodytes troglodytes hirtensis*) is resident on the small rocky group of islands in the Atlantic after which it is named.

Although on some islands the wren resides on open coasts, cliffs and moorland, it normally prefers habitats with a fair amount of vegetation, being particularly at home by lakesides and along streams fringed by trees. The wren is a common bird in woodland and hedgerow habitats. Wrens frequent suburban gardens in Britain and elsewhere in Europe, and numbers may be quite high if there is adequate cover. Out of the breeding season many resort to reed-beds, but few remain to nest.

Density figures have been calculated for a range of British habitats: typical values found in a 1972 study averaged 22.5 pairs per square kilometre for farmland, and 61.4 for woodland. Some woodland areas had 100 pairs per square kilometre. One estimate of the total British and Irish population was 10 million pairs, making the wren one of the most abundant British breeding species. Careful studies of the distribution of the species have found that it breeds almost everywhere in the British Isles, although, surprisingly, at the time of some surveys it was absent from the Scottish island of Tiree.

The North American subspecies, the winter wren, is more unobtrusive than its European counterpart, frequenting rocky glens, swamps and the borders of streams: it is shy and secretive. The widely distributed house wrens of the Americas, which, as the name implies, are more tolerant of the presence of humans, occupy areas that might otherwise accommodate winter wrens.

A bird's beak provides a good indication as to what it feeds upon, and hence of its adaptations linked with foraging. The beaks of St Kilda and Shetland wrens, subspecies inhabiting bleak environments, are thicker and stronger than those of mainland birds which forage in habitats where food is more abundant. The wing-length also increases, on the average, as one moves northwards from fertile mainland environments to bleak northern islands. Thus the physical form of the bird, its habitat — particularly its food supply — and many aspects of its breeding biology and behaviour are seen to be closely linked to one another.

FOOD AND FORAGING

The success of such a tiny and vulnerable bird in spreading throughout much of the world and occupying a wide range of habitats is largely due to its ability to forage where larger birds cannot go and to devour many kinds of creature. Great activity and small size go together in hummingbirds and sunbirds, for their energy output is great and needs constant fuelling. A wren is seldom still, except when it perches on a twig

6

preening or is brooding or roosting. Its flight is direct but most of its time is spent creeping through the undergrowth or flitting from twig to twig picking up small insects as it goes. Its long curved claws enable it to cling to the bark of trees and it is one of the few birds that will enter sheds, stables and other man-made structures seeking food. Wrens will enter houses through tiny cracks: in Iceland they pick at flitches of bacon hanging in dwellings. A wren is accustomed to going in and out of thickets, crevices, burrows and caves. Its small size, brownish colouration and frequent exploration of crevices among rocks have earned the wren of the Faroe Islands and Iceland the nickname 'brother of the mouse'. When snow lies thickly on herbage, wrens sometimes penetrate beneath, seeking food, but only infrequently do they visit bird tables, although in winter they are found about stables and cattle yards, finding not only food but roosting sites in such places. The wren's diet includes caterpillars, pupae, moths, mosquitoes and spiders. Although insects are its mainstay, it also occasionally eats earthworms and molluscs, and very occasionally a wren has been recorded catching small fish.

6. *Graph showing variation in wing-length in the wren from Scotland to Iceland.*

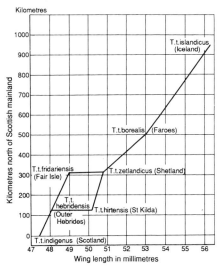

TERRITORY AND COMPETITION

Most birds, when breeding, defend an area around the nest or where the nest is going to be — the territory. This may be extensive or tiny. Gannets nesting close together on islands defend an area no larger than the sitting bird can reach with its beak, but a pair of eagles will treat an area of many hundreds of hectares as their private domain, from which other members of their species are excluded. Colonially nesting seabirds range far and wide over the ocean to collect prey; swallows, swifts and house martins similarly are aerial feeders. None of these species needs to defend extensive areas around its nests. In contrast, a species such as the wren, nesting sometimes where it is difficult to find enough food to satisfy a growing family, needs to exclude competitors of its own species.

There are species in which the female helps to defend the territory, but female wrens leave this responsibility to the males. The size of a wren's territory varies according to circumstances, including the character of the habitat and the amount of competition. After severe winters competition is much reduced and territories may be large, but during a succession of mild seasons numbers build up and territories are smaller. Thus in successive years after a hard winter the number of wren territories in Regent's Park, London, increased from five to six, eight, eleven and thirteen. Similarly, along a hedgerow the number of wrens increases and the lengths of their territories decrease after several mild winters. One study suggested that between 1964 (after two severe winters) and 1974 there was a tenfold increase in numbers in some English farmland habitats. The disparities in size between wren territories are illustrated by a comparison between an oakwood in Ireland, where there were 1.5 per hectare, and bleak moorland in Orkney, with one territory per 42 hectares.

Usually defiance by songs, calls and posturing is adequate for the defence of territory, but sometimes two males do fight. A wren will attack a stuffed dummy placed in its territory. In some species the males' mates join in but female wrens do not concern themselves with male quarrels. It is

7

7. A wren attacking a stuffed dummy.

most unusual for one bird to injure another in a serious fight, but two angry males have been observed by the author gripping each other by their claws and tumbling down a low roof.

SOCIAL AND CLUSTER ROOSTING

Many species of bird roost socially, especially those such as rooks, jackdaws and gulls which are social in their nesting and breeding activities. Starlings, being birds which feed in flocks, small or great, sometimes assemble on town buildings in such numbers that they become an insanitary nuisance. Partridges 'jug' in groups on the ground — thus one wakeful bird can give the alarm to its companions if it notices a predator approaching.

Already we have noted that wren numbers are much reduced during severe winters, but chances of survival are increased if a small bird not only resorts to a snug roosting place but is accompanied by others so that they can keep each other warm.

During mild weather wrens roost singly in suitable nooks — old nests, nestboxes, tangles of ivy, cavities in walls and trees. A wren may vary its roosting place in summer as there is little danger of being chilled, but in winter the choice of a suitable roost is a matter of life or death.

'Cluster roosting', as it is called, may begin as early as October, but usually starts later as a response to low temperatures. It may be continued until mid February. Wrens seek out not only nests of their own species but also the disused nests of other birds, along with other suitable nooks in which to take refuge. Songs and calls around dusk attract other wrens to join a male and follow him to the roost. When parties notice others making for a roost, the songs and calls serve as rallying signals, and quite large numbers may become involved. Disused house martins' nests may be chosen, and, as several of these are often close together, overflow accommodation is available where numbers exceed the capacity of a single nest. More than forty may

8. *The St Kilda wren (Troglodytes troglodytes hirtensis).*

9. *A St Kilda wren at its nest.*

appropriate adjoining nests, with as many as twenty-two in a single nest. Indeed an almost incredible sixty have been reported as occupying a nestbox: it took twenty minutes for the party to enter.

The duration of the urge to cluster-roost depends on weather conditions. In one instance, communal roosting began in November, but when mild conditions occurred towards the end of January the birds became quarrelsome and some tried to prevent others entering or to evict them. Sexual and territorial instincts that had been suppressed during the winter roosting period were becoming dominant. By the time territorial song becomes prominent and nest building commences, cluster roosting has been abandoned, and the nesting cycle is renewed.

RISING AND ROOSTING

The times when a bird flies out of its roost or goes to it are of interest. The time of emergence can be an indication of a bird's sexual maturity and ardour; also, the number of hours it spends away from the roost enables some judgement to be made as to whether or not it is hard-pressed for food. Around midsummer diurnal birds may go to roost relatively early because, unless they have young to feed, they have plenty of time to find food. But in winter daylight hours and food are short, so roosting is later in relation to sunset: at this time of year it is essential for birds to take full advantage of the hours when they can see well enough to capture small creatures. On overcast evenings roosting is earlier than on clear nights.

During the breeding season the length of a wren's active day is governed by how busy it has to be. One bird when incubating arose on average 4.5 minutes after sunrise, and retired 116.5 minutes before sunset, but when responsible for young she rose, again on average, 15.9 minutes before sunrise and retired only 5.3 minutes before sunset. However, in Shetland, with longer summer daylight, a pair ceased visiting the nest with food about twenty minutes before sunset. Generally females retire earlier than males and leave the roost later, but exceptions occur.

Calls and song

Calls are very varied. A churring call expresses excitement and is used as well as songs to signal to the young to follow the cock, and as a warning. A higher-pitched reeling chitter signals the presence of a ground predator, including a human. Various utterances attract the young to a snug roosting nook.

TERRITORIAL SONG

Three hundred years ago a writer, Nicholas Cox, quaintly described the wren's song: 'This bird, in my opinion is a pretty, sweet, dapper songster, being of a Nature cheerful; as he is pleasant to the ear, so he is to the Eye: and when he sings cocks up his Tail and throws out his notes with so much alacrity and pleasure that I know not any Bird of its bigness which more delights the sense of hearing.'

Experts in the analysis of sounds consider the song unmusical, but, however this may be, it is very pleasing, especially when listened to when no other birds are singing, as may happen during the winter. It is a rapid, lively, quite loud, very high-pitched phrase of about five or six seconds' duration, with a pause about as long between phrases so that there are about five or six phrases a minute. It is pitched around the highest note of the piano. So rapid are the notes that human ears are unable to distinguish them all separately. The phrase has been described as having an 'incomplete' or 'unfinished' character. Recordings of some subspecies have revealed 130 notes although human ears can detect only thirty to fifty — but there is much slurring.

There are few months of the year when the song may not be heard, although hard winter weather reduces the amount. Even in January a bird may sing, and in March there may be song for two or three hours in the morning — the period when the majority of songbirds are most vocal. Individual wrens can identify their neighbours by their songs.

All this is territorial song which indicates the bounds of a bird's territory and his position in it, warns other cocks not to trespass

10. *A wren in song.*

and invites females to approach, but the wren modifies his territorial song more than most birds according to circumstances. It is an identificatory, warning song, attractive so far as females are concerned, but under certain conditions it changes its pattern and significance.

AGGRESSIVE SONG

One of these patterns may be called 'aggressive song' or 'fighting song'. It is identificatory and challenging. When the wren is confronted by an opponent his normal song becomes rapid, abbreviated and congested — much as when two frenzied people quarrel they utter a stream of incoherent insults at each other. Loud churring or ticking notes are also used as threats. Normally such aggressive song is sufficient to deter an intruder but sometimes territory owners have to give place to intruders, or at least surrender some territory.

WHISPER SONG

This type of song varies from one or two quiet 'chit' notes to a series and is more commonly uttered by females than males. When it is sustained it is rather like the twittering of a distant swallow. It may be heard on various occasions. A female may give a few twitters before feeding small chicks, on alighting at the nest, or leading young from it. The author has heard it from a bird exploring a summerhouse, apparently seeking a roosting site, or from two males during a territorial dispute in October.

COURTSHIP AND NEST-INVITATION SONG

Wren courtship is very beautiful. When a male is courting he frequently sings his normal song phrase but at times it becomes modified into subsong, a slower, more subdued continuous utterance. This is among

11

11 (above left).   *Woodland wren habitat in eastern England.*

12 (above right).   *A wren in flight.*

13 (below).   *A wren (right), sharing a nesting box with a blue tit (Parus caeruleus) (left).*

14. *A wren feeding a young cuckoo (Cuculus canorus).*

15. *A wren removing faeces from its nest.*

the most delightful of bird songs, although few naturalists have stressed its charm. The notes follow each other melodiously and this meditative song is audible only a few metres from the singer. Very occasionally, when the bird maintains his gentle warbling for more than half a minute, it is heard to full perfection. Sometimes a cock may utter a fragment when visiting an unoccupied nest, as if anticipating partnership, but usually he warbles as he moves among the twigs above the apparently uninterested female.

Often this song is uttered as the male leads a female to a nearby nest, or as he perches outside it, with tail spread and wings aquiver, animatedly encouraging the female to enter. We must be wary of attributing to birds emotions like our own, but this courtship song has been compared to the soft endearments of lovers!

Breeding

NESTS AND NEST BUILDING

Comparatively few European birds — the magpie, dipper, house martin, long-tailed tit and some warblers — build enclosed nests similar in pattern to the wren's. This closed type has two advantages. First, the sitting bird, eggs and chicks are concealed in the perfectly camouflaged domed nest of withered leaves. Second, warmth is conserved better than in an open nest. The wren often takes advantage of a cavity in which to build its nests: it may build in some crevice in the root disc of a fallen tree or in a hollow tree-trunk, or sometimes the abandoned nest of another species is used. Nestboxes may be used, and foresters sometimes provide such boxes in new plantations to encourage insect-eating birds. A wren has been known

16. *A wren nesting in an old swallow's nest.*

17. *A wren at its nest in an ivy-covered stump.*

18. *A wren feeding its young: note the vivid yellow gaping beaks.*

to share a nestbox with a blue tit (*Parus caeruleus*). However, a wren can nest amongst twigs where there are no holes or cavities, and ivy climbing over a wall or old tree may conceal a nest. This adaptation has been of importance in enabling the species to spread throughout the large area it now occupies.

The nest is made of leaves and moss, neatly domed, often with the roof project-

ing slightly over the circular entrance, making it easier for a sitting bird to evade a predator by unexpectedly flying downwards. The threshold is made firm with dried grass stems, as it has to withstand much wear and tear, especially when, towards the end of the nestling period, the parents go in and out hundreds of times a day. The structure is compact: this is achieved by the use of damp material which, as it dries, binds firmly together. By making damp building material abundant, rainy weather stimulates the birds to build.

Normally the work is done by the cock, who prepares a home to which he will in due course invite a female. Especially in favourable habitats, he may construct as many as a dozen nests, some incomplete.

Originally it was probably the concealing rather than the heat-conserving properties of the wren's domed nest that were important, as the original stock came from America, in the warmer regions of which wren species are most numerous. In tropical forests there are many predadors: reptiles (including snakes), as well as birds and mammals, raid nests. Some weaver birds suspend their pouched nests from the tips of twigs, out of reach of monkeys. It seems possible that the practice of building a covered-in nest arose to frustrate predators in the tropics, and that when the wren invaded colder northern regions the domed nest not only served this purpose but also became important for conserving warmth. It also facilitated polygamy (see below), by

enabling a single parent to rear the brood. Moreover cluster roosting in such nests in winter makes it possible for the birds to survive severe weather.

Nests may be built not only amongst twigs and in crevices, but even in holes in the ground. The author knew of a disused bicycle bag hanging in a summerhouse that was used several years in succession and he once found a nest in the remains of a sparrowhawk on a gamekeeper's gibbet. He has seen another in a coil of rope, and yet another in a human skull. Other naturalists have reported nests in the carapace of a tortoise, the fold of a curtain, and in a pair of trousers hung out to dry. There is an ancient story about St Malo that rings true. Returning one day from pruning the monastery's vines, he found that a wren had built in the cloak he had left hanging on a bush. Considerately, he did not retrieve the cloak until the young had fledged. Cock wrens visit unoccupied nests, keeping them in repair.

Wrens build energetically but take time off to feed, sing and patrol their territory between building spells, each of which may

19. *Domed wrens' nests. Note the construction from leaves, grass, twigs and moss.*

20. *A wren near its domed nest.*

last for twenty minutes. The amount of time spent working tends to decrease during the day and on successive days but variations occur, depending on the bird's energy and such distractions as courting a female, singing against an intruder and foraging. Building tends to be most energetic during the first two days, but a wren visits his unoccupied nests from time to time, adjusting a leaf here and there. In the intervals between periods of fetching material and building, the wren sings, so that nests may be found where occasional bursts of song are heard.

In Britain, Holland, Denmark and other countries in western Europe, nest building begins in early March and continues for some months. For example, during the last few days of March and early April, one wren visited and took over old nests built by a predecessor, began a nest of his own on 9th April, another on 13th April, and yet others on 27th April, 21st and 27th May and 3rd June. Out-of-season nest building may occur, exceptionally, as late as November. In harsh habitats, such as St Kilda, fewer nests are built than in more fertile environments.

Although nest construction is the male's responsibility, very occasionally a female may collaborate and even seem to embarrass a male by doing so. When a female selects a nest she may, at first, take in a leaf or two, but she busies herself finding and fetching lining material to make a soft downy mattress of feathers and hairs. In Alaska fox fur and reindeer hairs are used. Nest lining may be completed in two days, but it may take longer and may indeed continue to some extent after the eggs have been laid and the bird is already sitting. Females are expert in finding feathers where the human eye can detect few, but in places such as a poultry yard a nest may be stuffed to overflowing with them.

THE PAIR-BOND

Before the unusual character of the wren's pair-bond was understood, the extra nests were called 'play nests' or 'cock's nests', and it was supposed that they were accounted for by the building impulse 'getting out of hand'. Egg collectors long ago noticed that some nests were never occupied. Only recently has the explanation of this unusual practice been discovered.

The wren is unusual among European birds in being polygamous. A cock may have two or three mates at one time and therefore needs to have unoccupied nests to show late-comers. Moreover, females avoid using, for their second brood, nests which have already been occupied. Used nests may become infested with vermin or become known to predators.

A bird's activities are related to one another as components of a system. Polygamy involves securing a territory providing sufficient food to enable a bird mated to

a bigamous male to nourish the brood. A number of nests must be provided so that the females may have sufficient choice, and a long season of song is necessary to deter trespassers and attract females to partner the males during first and second broods. But subspecies differ, and in harsh habitats — on barren islands and in the tundra, for example — fewer nests are built, second broods are less usual, the song season is less prolonged and polygamy is rare. The males sing and build less, as they have to devote more time to foraging and gathering food for the young than in woodland. Polygamy is an adaptation to fertile, productive or 'lush' habitats; monogamy is necessary where living is more difficult, in 'bleak' environments. Such adaptability is rare among birds and may partially explain the wren's success.

We can now understand why cock wrens sing so much, build so many nests, visit them regularly and keep them in repair. A well built, concealed nest is more likely to be attractive to a female than a neglected structure — and it should be remembered that in favourable habitats many wrens have a second brood.

EGGS AND EGG LAYING

In Britain the clutch is usually five or six eggs, but, as with some other species, the number tends to be larger in northern regions, where longer periods of summer daylight enable foraging to continue longer each day. In Spain there are commonly five eggs whereas in Norway the number is from six to eight. In *Twelfth Night* (act 3, scene 2, line 70) Shakespeare mentions 'the youngest wren of nine' but such a large family would be exceptional. He may have been influenced by folklore. Second-brood layings in Britain tend to be smaller than earlier clutches and may consist of no more than four eggs. They are white, spotted with brownish red, particularly at the large end. A typical female weighs about 9-10 grams, and thus a full clutch of five or six eggs, each weighing about 1.5 grams, represents 85-95 per cent of the body weight of the mother.

It is much easier to observe the laying and brooding procedure of open-nesting birds than is possible with wrens. Wrong assumptions may easily be made: for example, it is mistaken to believe that because a bird spends the night in a cavity nest she must be brooding. Some birds, such as the redstart, first stand over their eggs.

The author and a friend overcame some of the difficulties of observation by arranging an automatic device at nests which recorded the birds' comings and goings, and they fixed a thermometer with the bulb below the eggs, but readable outside. They sought to discover whether a wren spends the night in the nest and then lays, or whether she roosts outside and then visits to deposit the egg. It was found that the behaviour of birds varied. At one nest the wren left for a short period about sunrise and then returned to lay; at another the female came to the nest from her roost elsewhere to deposit the egg, and at yet another the bird varied in her behaviour, returning to the nest to lay the second, third and fourth eggs but laying the fifth egg without leaving. At yet another nest no records were obtained until after the third egg had been laid, but the next three were laid before the morning sortie. Such variability shows that in studying the details of a bird's behaviour it is unwise to generalise from a few observations, but it demonstrates the interest of intensive study.

INCUBATION

The eggs are almost always incubated entirely by the female. Books summing up the incubation periods of birds either state 'about so many days' or give a range of periods, as in the case of the wren: 'Period usually 14-15 days, 13 and 16 recorded'. But any records concerning closed-nesting species are open to question unless an automatic recorder is used. The apparatus used by the author and his friend enabled them to ascertain how incubation began at four wrens' nests and showed that, as with laying behaviour, this can vary greatly. A bird that laid her first egg on 6th May increased the amount of brooding day by day but did not establish the regular routine until 16th May. In contrast, another wren in June was incubating, with regular periods on and off, the day her fifth and last egg was laid — apart from one unusually long absence, perhaps owing to the intrusion of a predator. During the day a spell of thirty minutes on the nest, followed by ten or twelve minutes away, might be typical. Thus it is difficult to state exactly how long wrens' eggs are incubated, but at two nests the interval from the beginning of regular incubation until the hatching of the third chick was fifteen days. Until incubation is continuous, there is little development of the embryo in a bird's egg. Records of longer incubation periods may be explained

21. *Integration of the activities of the wren, (A) in fertile woodland and garden habitats, and (B) in bleak environments such as the Atlantic islands.*

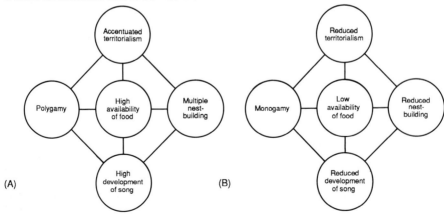

20

22. *'Fertile' wren habitat: English oak woodland.*

as owing to full incubation having been delayed. Eggs remain fertile even when three or four days elapse before incubation begins.

It is known that unhatched chicks communicate with each other by making clicking sounds in the egg, resulting in the eggs hatching closer together in time. As this is true of birds as different as the quail and the great tit, it may also be true of the wren. Commonly wrens' eggs all hatch within a few hours, and the egg shells are carried some distance away.

BEHAVIOUR WHEN A NEST IS ROBBED

The recording apparatus was operating at a nest when it was rifled and so the bird's reaction to this disaster was discovered. The nest was in an ivy-clad trunk and invisible from below, suggesting that a predator may find nests by watching the owner's activities. The culprit was a cat, white hairs in the ivy identifying it as a particular white Persian. The fourth and final egg had been laid on 22nd June and the numbers of feeding sorties made by the incubating bird on successive days had been 36, 36, 36, 33 and 38. On the day of the raid (which occurred at about one o' clock in the afternoon) the wren had visited the nest 22 times before the disaster but afterwards the recorder showed that she went to it eleven times during the rest of the day. Thus in spite of the fright the bird must have suffered and the destruction of the nest and eggs, her in-built rhythm of activity continued and she maintained a frequency of visits not far short of her usual routine.

PREDATION AND PARASITISM

Although wrens' nests are well hidden, it is estimated that about a third of them come to grief in one way or another. It is unusual for anyone to be on the spot when a nest is robbed, and so not much is known about which predators are responsible. A weasel has been seen emerging from a nest after eating the young and some nests are so low that rats could enter them. Some nests are destroyed by magpies and jays: they watch the movements of the bird and tear the nest open from the top. Sparrowhawks also occasionally seize a wren.

Sometimes a nest becomes so infested with mites that the young die or fledge in a debilitated condition.

Cuckoos (*Cuculus canorus*) in Britain and Ireland, as well as in other countries, sometimes lay in a wren's nest. By keeping watch on the birds they find nests, even when they are in such concealed niches as the dark corner of a shed. As observers have reported seeing only one wren active at a nest containing a young cuckoo which fledged successfully, it seems that the efforts of such a bird are sufficient to rear the usurper — no mean achievement for such a tiny foster parent. The successful expulsion by the blind, newly hatched cuckoo of the foster parents' eggs through a comparatively small aperture is also a notable feat. The young cuckoo becomes enormous in relation to the size of its foster parent.

THE NESTLING PERIOD

Wren chicks are naked and blind when hatched. They are able to do little more than raise their heads and open their beaks to be fed. Usually only the female feeds them during the first few days, and she spends a good deal of time covering and

21

23. *'Bleak' wren habitat: tundra in northern Sweden.*

warming them. Faeces may be removed from the nest. When, as she generally does, she has a polygamous mate who may be busy courting another female, building a nest or, perhaps, feeding another brood, she may receive little or no help with rearing her chicks. The number of visits with food steadily increases if all goes well and may reach between five hundred and six hundred a day for three or four days towards the end of the nestling period (even when only one bird is feeding the young), but much depends on whether foraging is easy or not. The tempo can be rapid during caterpillar plagues or near water where mosquitoes and other insects are plentiful. At first the parent or parents have to enter the nest but towards fledging the young come to the entrance to be fed and, especially when hungry, call loudly enough to risk betraying their whereabouts to predators. Here we have another example of the network of adaptations in which food supply is important. Scarcity may lead to the undernourishment and debility of the chicks and also thus increases their vulnerability, but counterbalancing this is the effect of competition between the hungry young, with only the most vigorous surviving, to the advantage of the species.

As already noted, cock wrens in bleak areas, such as some of the North Atlantic islands where food is not so readily available as in English woodland, farm and hedgerow environments, give their mates more help in tending the nestlings. Without their help it is doubtful whether all the chicks could be reared successfully. Birds of these subspecies have not evolved the alternative of laying fewer eggs but, as we have seen, there are more daylight hours for foraging in the summers of higher latitudes. But what happens in southern woodland, where about half the males are bigamous, when a female is unable to cope because of failing energy, difficulties in finding enough prey, or is wounded or killed? The recording apparatus enabled this question to be answered. At one nest, when the daily visits of the female to the nest began to become inadequate, her mate came to the rescue and increased his visits so that day by day the chicks were fed about the normal number of times. Then, when his mate recovered, she took over for the last few days and all was well. At another nest the female disappeared, perhaps because of some injury. The young had hatched on 18th July and the male had fed them only occasionally. On the morning and early afternoon of the 25th, both took part in the feeding, but early in the afternoon the hen's visits decreased and after half past three she came no more. Her mate, stimulated by the begging calls of the young, became increasingly attentive and behaved like a female; he sang no more and devoted himself so completely to the needs of the nestlings that he perched on the author's finger at the entrance to the nest, not noticing that his perch was part of a human! He even spent a night — probably several — in the nest with the family, most unusual behaviour for a male. Unfortunately he was unable to cope with the situation successfully. One chick died on 27th July and another the next day, but the others fledged after spending a day longer in the nest than the chicks in two other nests close by. Thus the inclination of a male wren to mate with two or three females does not prevent his coming to the rescue when a brood is menaced by starvation. He can switch from patrolling his territory, warning off neighbours and seeking another mate to become a most attentive parent — a very different situation from that observed at a robin's nest, where after the cock's mate died he looked into the nest only occasionally and left the young to die, although they were on the point of fledging.

THE CHICKS' FOOD SUPPLY

According to the character of the environment and other conditions, the food provided for the young varies. In some areas and seasons it may consist mainly of common, easily obtainable organisms such as mosquitoes or caterpillars (the latter especially during caterpillar plagues that infest the foliage of some trees). But nonetheless birds specialising in one kind of prey will take quite different creatures when they come across them as they forage. Shetland wrens, perhaps even more than other subspecies, may bring an assortment of prey to the nestlings. On the last day a brood spent in the nest, successive rations consisted of a noctuid moth, a crane-fly and a green caterpillar. Earlier in the same day one beakload consisted of a centipede and some small insects. Pupae and spiders may also be brought. During their last day or two in the nest the youngsters disgorged rufous brown matter, which fell on a stone below. Microscopic examination revealed that it consisted of the fragmented indigestible parts of small creatures, including the wing scales of moths, the integuments of insect larvae, fragments of a caddis fly, parts of the wings of a chalchid wasp, the jaws of a centipede and fragments of beetles. The young fledged successfully in spite of this miscellaneous diet. Perhaps the disgorging of indigestible material is commoner than is usually realised, for it is well known that owls, and occasionally other species, eject pellets or castings consisting of the fur, bones or other hard parts of their prey.

FLEDGING

The nestling period usually lasts sixteen days. It may be a day or two longer or shorter, depending on the rate of the chicks' development, and this in turn is related to the number to be fed, whether both parents take part, the availability of food and how nourishing it is. The young may leave haphazardly or follow one another rather quickly. When they are ready the mother may perch excitedly outside, with tail erect, encouraging them to leave. If alarmed, several may flit out together, thus bewildering the predator that disturbed them. They are able to fly a little and utter chittering calls if disquieted, and a squeak at other times, expressing their hunger and enabling the parent to find them quickly. The cock is often on the scene when the young emerge, but if this is his first brood he may appear more interested in his mate than the young, singing a brief phrase to her. The fledglings' squeaking also serves to keep members of the brood in touch so they can roost together. The length of time that a female feeds her fledged brood varies, depending on whether she has started another brood, but a cock can look after them for a fortnight or even longer. Altogether young wrens receive parental care for about thirty days — longer than many small perching birds.

The fledged young of most small birds are left to look after themselves at night, but wren parents are more attentive. Towards dusk, sometimes earlier, the parent begins uttering calls and if the cock is taking responsibility he sometimes sings as well, moving towards the roost in short flights. Sometimes a male may have to make considerable efforts to induce them to follow. He may fly time and again across a road to persuade them. When he reaches the nook to serve as dormitory he moves about, singing near it and sometimes creeping in and out as he did earlier in the season trying to induce his mate to choose a nest. After they have all entered he goes off to roost elsewhere, but a female may go inside, if an unoccupied wren's nest has been chosen, to share the limited space and help to keep the family warm. The family may resort to the roosting place nightly for as long as a fortnight.

Young wrens sometimes settle in dormitories of their own choosing, perhaps the open deserted nest of a blackbird or thrush. A brood has also been known to huddle together precariously on the floor of a shed.

FOSTERING

The term 'fostering' serves to describe a different kind of situation from that created by the cuckoo — parasitisation. This behaviour is not very unusual and occurs when a bird voluntarily feeds young other than its own. It may happen when a bird loses its own nestlings or has an exceptionally strong drive to offer food, sometimes when the impulse develops prematurely, or on occasions when the sight or sound of nestlings begging to be fed attracts the attention of a bird taking food to its own young. A wren entered a hide where a photographer was taking pictures of a young willow warbler outside, then went away and returned with food for the chick. Another wren fed two newly fledged spotted flycatchers close to its own nest and a male has been observed feeding nestling great tits with greater diligence than their parents. The reverse situation may occur: a robin has been seen feeding young wrens.

Further reading

Armstrong, E. A. *The Wren*. Collins, 1955.

Armstrong, E. A., and Whitehouse, H. K. L. 'Behavioural Adaptations of the Wren (*Troglodytes troglodytes*)', *Biological Review*, 52 (1977), 235-94.

Boyd, J. M. 'The Birds of Tiree and Coll', *British Birds*, 51 (1958), 41-56 and 103-18.

Hawthorn, I., and Mead, C. J. 'Wren Movements and Survival', *British Birds*, 68 (1975), 349-58.

Williamson, K. 'Population and Breeding Environment of the St Kilda and Fair Isle Wrens', *British Birds*, 51 (1958), 369-93.

Williamson, K. 'Habitat Preferences of the Wren on English Farmland', *Bird Study*, 16 (1969), 53-9.

ACKNOWLEDGEMENTS

Photographs are acknowledged as follows: Edward A. Armstrong, 1, 17, 19, 20 and 23; Patrick H. Armstrong, 11 and 22; R. P. Gait, 10; Eric and David Hosking, cover and 7, 8, 9, 12, 13, 16 and 18; Michael Leach, 14 and 15. Guy Foster drew the maps and diagrams. Parts of this work were originally published in Danish by Gad AV Media, Copenhagen.